Key Words
Reading

D1625531

1a
Play with us

written by W. Murray
illustrated by J.H. Wingfield

Peter   Jane

a dog   a tree   a ball

toys   a shop

Readers will get the most out of the **Key Words** reading scheme when they follow the books in the pattern 1a, 1b, 1c: 2a, 2b, 2c: and so on.

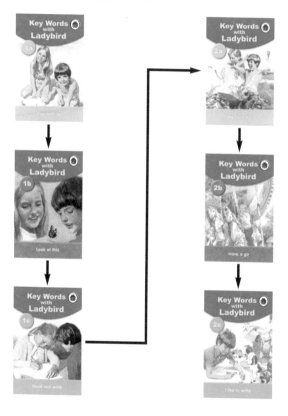

The a, b, and c series are all written using the same carefully controlled vocabulary.

The Ladybird Key Words Reading Scheme
has three series, each containing
twelve books.

The 'a' series gradually introduces and
repeats new words.

The parallel 'b' series provides further
practice of these words, but in a different
context and with different illustrations.

The 'c' series uses familiar words to teach
phonics in a methodical way, enabling
children to read more difficult words.
It also provides a link to writing.

All three series are written using the same
carefully controlled vocabulary.

Published by Ladybird Books Ltd
A Penguin Company
Penguin Books Ltd., 80 Strand, London WC2R 0RL, UK
Penguin Books Australia Ltd., Camberwell, Victoria, Australia
Penguin Books (NZ) Ltd., Private Bag 102902, NSMC, Auckland, New Zealand

21 23 25 27 29 30 28 26 24 22

ISBN-13: 978-1-8442-2360-2
Printed in China

Peter

Jane

a dog

a tree

a ball

toys

a shop

Peter

new word   Peter

Jane

Jane

Peter and Jane

---

new word

and

here is Peter

and

here is Jane

---

here is

Peter is here

and

Jane is here.

Here is

the dog.

Here   the   dog

Here is Jane and here is the dog.

Jane likes
the dog
and
Peter likes
the dog.

---

new word

likes

The dog
likes Jane
and
the dog
likes Peter.

The

I like Peter.

I like Jane.

I like

the dog.

Here is

a shop.

---

a shop

Here is

a toy shop.

I like

the toy shop.

---

toy

Peter is in

the toy shop.

new word

in

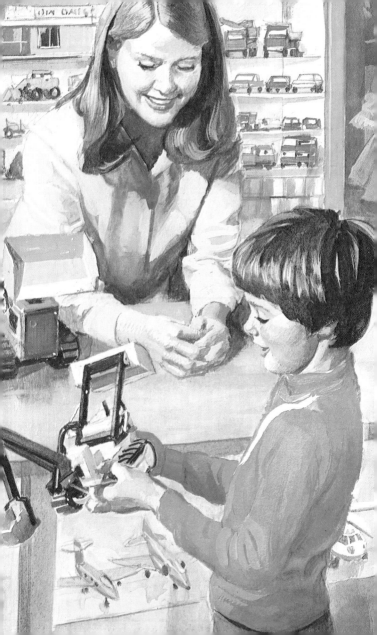

Jane is in
the toy shop.

The dog is in the toy shop.

Peter has a toy

and

Jane has a toy.

---

new word

has

Peter has a ball.

Peter likes

the ball.

ball

Here is the dog.
The dog has
the ball.

Here is a tree.

The ball is in

the tree.

---

new word

tree

Peter is in

the tree and

Jane is in

the tree.

Here is Peter

in the tree.

Peter has

the ball.

Now read book 1b

New words used in this book

Total number of new words: 16
Average repetition per word: 10